Cricket in a Thicket

Illustrations by

Feodor

Rojankovsky

AILEEN FISHER

Cricket

in a Thicket

CHARLES SCRIBNER'S SONS

New York

√8 | |
F 533 cr

GRATEFUL ACKNOWLEDGMENT IS MADE TO *My Weekly Reader*
AND *The Instructor*, WHERE SOME OF THE POEMS IN THIS
BOOK WERE FIRST PUBLISHED.

Printed in the United States of America
Library of Congress Catalog Card Number 63-14337

F-11.66(AJ)

CONTENTS

Six Legs and Eight   7

Four Legs and Two   19

*Sunflowers High
        and Pumpkins Low*   31

Warm Days and Cold   45

INDEX   63

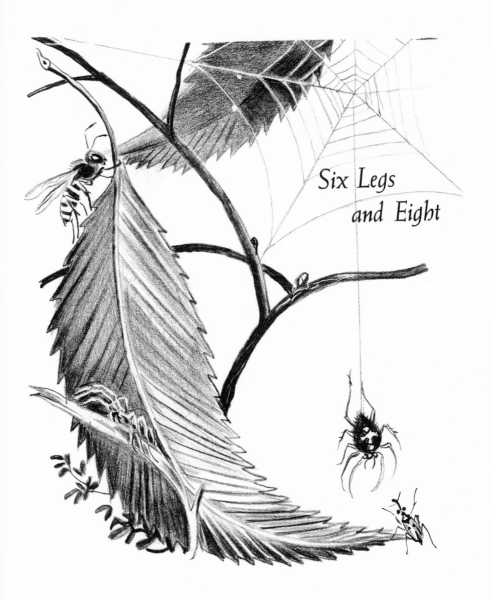

Six Legs
and Eight

Feet

Feet of snails
are only one.
Birds grow two
to hop and run.
Dogs and cats
and cows grow four.
Ants and beetles
add two more.
Spiders run around
on eight,
which may seem
a lot, but wait —
Centipedes
have more than *thirty*
feet to wash
when they get dirty.

Caterpillars

What do caterpillars do?
Nothing much but chew and chew.

What do caterpillars know?
Nothing much but how to grow.

They just eat what by and by
will make them be a butterfly,

But that is more than I can do
however much I chew and chew.

Like a Bug

Do you ever wonder
what it's like to be a bug,

Fitted in a jacket
that is stiff and rather snug,

Sleeping in a thistle
or beneath a leafy rug,

Never having gingersnaps
or cocoa in a mug,

Or a father you can talk to,
or a puppy you can hug?

Spider

I saw a little spider
with the smartest spider head.
She made — somewhere inside her —
a magic silken thread.

I saw her sliding down it.
She dangled in the air.
I saw her climbing up it
and pulling up each stair.

She made it look so easy
I wished all day I knew
how *I* could spin a magic thread
so I could dangle too.

Bedtime

Ladybugs haven't a house to sweep
or a bed to make or a yard to keep,
so at night
they stay where they are to sleep,
on a twig or leaf or stem.

Butterflies, folding their wings up tight,
sleep in the grass when day turns night,
down where it's dark
and out of sight,
down near the meadow's hem.

Bumblebees hurry when day is through
to crawl in a blossom pink or blue
or yellow or white,
and fragrant too. . . .
I'd rather sleep like them.

Jungles of Grass

Walking through the tangle
of grass and roots
and leaves that dangle
above the shoots,
ants and beetles
are certainly clever
not to get lost
forever and ever.

Cracker Time

Beetle,
you look so little
to be wandering off so far.

Don't you
think your mother
must be wondering where you are?

Beetle,
you must be hungry.
It is cracker time for me.

Do you
keep a cracker
in a pocket I can't see?

A Cricket

In a matchbox
is a cricket
with a patent-leather shine.
It's at Peter's,
and he's printed
MISTER CRICKET on a sign.

In a fruit jar
that is open,
with a leaf on which to dine,
is a cricket
that is Kathy's
and she thinks it's very fine.

Nothing's gayer
than a cricket!
Nothing's louder after nine!
But my mother
thinks a *thicket*
is the nicest place for mine.

16

Grasshoppers

Did ever you hear
of a funnier thing
than Mr. Grasshopper's
way to sing —
by rubbing his leg
against his wing?

Did ever you hear
of a thing in years
more queer than the way
Miss Grasshopper hears —
by using her legs
where she keeps her ears?

Four Legs
and Two

Birthday Present

White?
Oh yes, a woolly white one.

Black?
Oh yes, a black-as-night one.

Tan?
I think a tan or brown one
perfect for a farm or town one.

Sleek?
Oh yes, a sleek and trim one.

Shaggy?
Any her or him one.
Tousled, frowzled,
big or small,
I'd like any kind at all —
just so it's a *dog*.

Deer Mouse

Who tells the little deer mouse
when summer goes away
that she should fix a cozy place,
a comfy place to stay,
and fill her cupboard shelves with seeds
from berries, weeds, and hay?

Who tells the little deer mouse
before the year is old
that she should wear a warmer coat
to shield her from the cold?
I'm glad that *someone* tells her
and she does as she is told.

Moles

Don't you feel sorry
for grubby old moles,
always in tunnels,
always in holes,
never out watching
the sun climb high
or the grass bend low
or the wind race by
or stars make twinkles
all over the sky?

23

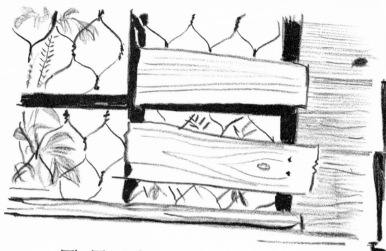

The Turtledoves

Mr. Turtledove and wife
live a most devoted life.
Back and forth they softly coo:
"Love to you."
And "Love to you."

Mr. Turtledove and spouse
share the work around the house,
taking turns to brood the eggs,
taking turns to stretch their legs.

Mr. Turtledove and wife
lead a very active life.
Oh, the bugs they have to catch
when the turtledovelets hatch!

But Mr. T. and Mrs. too,
even when there's work to do,
don't forget to nod and coo:
"Love to you."
And "Love to you."

The Ducklings

Fluffy, yellow, and trim,
only a few days old,
little ducklings can swim,
and never once are told:
"Paddle, and sit up tall,
wiggle your feet like so."
They don't have to learn at all.
They just *know*.

At Night

In the still dark depths
of the pines and birches,
day-birds sleep
on their hidden perches.

A woodchuck curls
in his burrow bed,
a squirrel in his leaf-nest
overhead.

And down in his tunnel
a chippy is dozing,
comfy and quiet
and never supposing
that out in the starlight
a doe and a fawn
are picking his daisies
and mowing his lawn!

The Handiest Nose

An elephant's nose
is the handiest nose,
the handiest nose of all—
it curves and sways
in the cleverest ways,
and trumpets a bugle call;
it reaches high
in the leafy sky
for bunches of leaves to eat,
and snuffs around
all over the ground,
and dusts the elephant's feet.

An elephant's nose
is the dandiest nose,

the handiest nose of all
for holding a palm,
when the day is calm,
as an elephant's parasol,
and making a spray
for a sultry day,
and a hose for sprinkling, too,
and a hand to wag
near your peanut bag
when you watch him at the zoo.

Oh, an elephant's nose
is fun to see,
an elephant's nose is fine;
it's clever as ever
a nose can be
but I'm glad it isn't *mine*.

In the Dark of Night

A mouse goes out
in the dark of night
without a lantern
or other light.
She's not afraid
of the dark at all,
though the night's so big
and herself so small.

Sunflowers High

and

Pumpkins Low

Seeds

Seeds know just the way to start —
I wonder how they get so smart.

They *could* come up in garden beds
feet first — by standing on their heads.

They *could* forget if they should grow
like sunflowers, high, or pumpkins, low.

They *could* forget their colors, too,
and yet they never, never do.

Grasses

Do you ever wonder
if horses and such
like all grasses
equally much?

Or are some grasses
like spinach and prunes
and others like
coconut macaroons?

33

The Daffodils

The daffodils, the daffodils,
they plan it all ahead;
they know what they should bottle up
to take along to bed.

They know that they will sleep for months
till cold and snow are gone,
and so they bottle sunshine up
before they start to yawn.

And then, when spring is not-quite warm
and days are not-quite mellow,
they poke up little goblets full
of yellow, yellow, yellow.

Stay-at-Home

If I were a stay-at-home
flower or clover,
I'd like a butterfly
coming over,
or a hungry moth,
or a honeybee,
to trade me news
for a cup of tea.

Pussy Willows

Every spring the pussy willows
come in such a hurry
I am sure we'd shake our heads,
I am sure we'd worry,
if they didn't wear their coats
buttoned tight around their throats,
sleek and warm and furry.

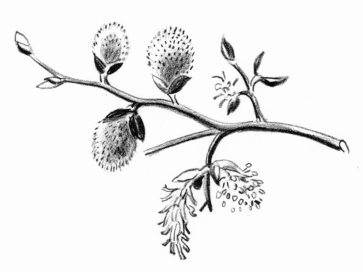

Dandelions Everywhere

The wind had some seeds
in his hand one day,
and he tripped on a bush
when he came our way.

He tripped on a bush
in our yard, he did,
and he dropped the seeds —
and they ran and hid.

They ran and hid
in the grass and clover
and didn't come out
till March was over.

And now that they're out
we've more than our share
of dandelions,
     dandelions,
         everywhere.

Counting Petals

Somehow, flowers
have learned the trick
of practicing arithmetic:

Easter lilies
don't count far —
one, two, three their petals are.

Yellow poppies
count one more.
Roses count to one plus four.

How did dandelions
and such
ever learn to count so *much?*

Trees

Trees just stand around all day
and sun themselves and rest.

They never walk or run away,
and surely that is best.

For otherwise how would a squirrel
or robin find its nest?

Best of All

Trees are short
and trees are tall,
and some grow leaves
to scuff in fall.

Trees are fat
and trees are thin
with windows where
the sun looks in.

Trees are big
and trees are small—
but *Christmas* trees
are best of all.

Pine Music

The pine has a harp
in its house of green,
a golden harp,
but it can't be seen
except by the wind
who strums the strings
for the listening ears
of rabbits and things.

Warm Days
and Cold

As Soon As It's Fall

Rabbits and foxes
as soon as it's fall
get coats that are warm
with no trouble at all,
coats that are furry
and woolly and new,
heavy and thick
so the cold can't get through.

They don't have to buy them
or dye them or try them,
they don't have to knit them
or weave them or fit them,
they don't have to sew them
or stitch them all through,

They just have to *grow* them,
and that's what they do.

Fall of the Year

Out of the trees
with rustly sleeves
fall wonderful colorful
autumn leaves.

Out of the weeds
fall countless seeds,
the kind of food
that a snowbird needs.

Out of the boughs
fall nuts and fruits
without any bump-saving
parachutes.

Everything falls
from There to Here....
no wonder we call it
the fall of the year.

Warning

"It's time," Autumn said to the hollyhocks.
"It's time," to the grapevines creeping.
"You've grown so tall
and spready and all,
it's time you did some sleeping."

"It's time," Autumn said to the goldenrod.
"It's time," to the grass and clover,
"to get in your beds
and cover your heads
and sleep till the cold is over."

The West Wind

The west wind was a thief one day —
he stole the maples' lockets.
The elm trees' jewels he snatched away
and stuffed them in his pockets.
He pulled the poplars' spangles down
and dropped them as he hurried
across the fields beyond the town,
but not a soul was worried.

"He steals the leaves," a robin sang,
"and then away he chases.
But in the spring he'll come and hang
some new ones in their places."

Going South So Soon

Between the green of summer
and the white of snow,
what a burst of colors
all the treetops show!

I'm sure the wrens and swallows
who nested here in June
don't know what they're missing —
going south so soon.

Autumn Bluebirds

They twitter gentle little rhymes
and hang around the door.
They say goodbye a dozen times,
then settle down once more.

They flash their blue against the gold
of stubble-field and hill,
and chirp, "Tomorrow may be cold."
And yet they linger still.

Then, suddenly, with snow-clouds blown
across the purple haze,
we find that we are left alone
with chickadees and jays.

All Winter

Don't you feel sorry
for woodchucks and frogs,
and turtles way down
at the bottom of bogs,
and chipmunks in burrows
and toads under logs,
not to wake up all winter!

With skating and sliding
and snow by the mile
and Christmas arriving
in just a short while,
don't you feel happy
it isn't *our* style
not to wake up all winter?

Spring Song

A meadow lark came back one day
and searched beneath the faded hay
out in the rocks, beside a cleft,
to find a song that he had left.

He found it. And he tried it out.
He tossed the melody about,
and not a note was hurt a bit
by winter drifting over it.

On Time

"Set your watch," the weather said.
"See those doings up ahead —
stirrings in the crocus bed,
bluebirds on the wing,
sun a ball of golden thread,
maple tips a-swelling red.
"Set your watch," the weather said,
"half a tick to spring!"

Time for Rabbits

"Look!" says the catkin
in its gray hatkin.
"Look!" say the larks and sparrows.
"The pasture is stirring,
the willows are purring,
and sunlight is shooting its arrows."

"Look!" wind is humming.
"Easter is coming.
Hear how the brooklet rushes.
It's time for the rabbits
with Easter-egg habits
to get out their paints and brushes."

Summer Days

Sunflowers
stretch to watch the sun,
vines of pumpkins creep.

Poppies
fold their parasols
at night and go to sleep.

Pansies
in their velvet gowns
sit calmly in the shade.

Water lilies
have the fun —
they go out to wade.

At the End of the Field

I wonder who lives
at the end of the field
where shadows of summer quiver?

I wonder who lives
at the end of the path
on the bank of the autumn river?

And I wonder, I wonder
who lives in the sky
on a star or a planet
a million miles high,
and if I will ever
get up there to see
if *they* wonder much
about people like me.

INDEX

All Winter, 54-55

As Soon As It's Fall, 46

At Night, 27

At the End of the Field, 60-61

Autumn Bluebirds, 53

Bedtime, 12

Best of All, 43

Birthday Present, 20

Caterpillars, 9

Counting Petals, 40

Cracker Time, 15

Cricket, A, 16

Daffodils, The, 34

Dandelions Everywhere, 39

Deer Mouse, 22

Ducklings, The, 26

Fall of the Year, 48

Feet, 8

Going South So Soon, 52

Grasses, 33

Grasshoppers, 18

Handiest Nose, The, 28-29

In the Dark of Night, 30

Jungles of Grass, 14

Like a Bug, 10

Moles, 23

On Time, 57

Pine Music, 44

Pussy Willows, 37

Seeds, 32

Spider, 11

Spring Song, 56

Stay-at-Home, 36

Summer Days, 59

Time for Rabbits, 58

Trees, 41

Turtledoves, The, 24-25

Warning, 49

West Wind, The, 50-51